# A Nurturing Father's Journal

## *Developing Attitudes and Skills for Male Nurturance*

D1616762

# Workbook

by Mark Perlman, MA

Center for Growth & Development, Inc. Publishing
3277 Fruitville Road – 1D
Sarasota, Florida 34237
Toll Free 1-888-390-1119
www.facebook.com/nurturingfathers

# A Nurturing Father's Journal

*Developing Attitudes and Skills for Male Nurturance*

## Workbook

by Mark Perlman, MA

The **Nurturing Father's Journal** is a workbook designed to be utilized in **The Nurturing Father's Program** with the Facilitator's Manual and other materials. For additional information on **The Nurturing Father's Program,** contact:

**Center for Growth & Development, Inc.**
**3277 Fruitville Road – 1D, Sarasota, Florida 34237**

**Toll Free 1-888-390-1119**
**Fax: 941-953-9552**
**E-mail: mcperl@verizon.net**


ISBN# 0-9662927-0-7


Printed and bound in the United States of America.

10   9   8   7   6   5   4   3   2   1

Dedication

*To Barney, my father,*
*and nurturing male role model,*

*To my wonderful sons,*
*Jaime and Corey,*
*with whom I have learned and grown;*

*and to all the men dedicated*
*to being nurturing fathers.*

## Acknowledgments

To Kate McPhillips, my wife and partner, for her love, support, wisdom and dedication;

Stephen Bavolek, father of the **Nurturing Programs for Parents and Children,** nurturing ambassador, and mentor;

Vicki Rollo, book design and illustration;

John Marcus, editor, consultant (and pizza lover);

Lisa Paulson, word processing and computer assistance;

Alan Glassberg, Jim Burns, Vinny Boyle for field testing the program and helping to shape the final outcome;

Phyllis Perlman (thanks for everything, Mom);

Alan Perlman, music and brotherhood;

Trout, for the use of his relevant and insightful cartoon;

Janet Perlman (co-parent), Jared and Alice Massanari, Marc Weinberg, Joe Ferrandino, Fran Kaplan, Paul Burns, Alice Taylor, Judy Ruf, Margo Burchim-Glassberg, Peter Howard, Ishmael Katz, Bill and Carol McPhillips, valued friends, colleagues, and extended family;

The Monday Night Men's Group; and the Father's United Network (FUN) of Sarasota, Florida.

*When men abandon the upbringing*
*of their children to their wives,*
*a big loss is suffered by themselves.*
*For what they lose is the possibility of growth*
*in themselves for being human,*
*which the stimulation of bringing up*
*one's children gives.*

– Ashley Montague
Anthropologist, 1964

# A Nurturing Father's Journal for Developing Attitudes and Skills for Male Nurturance

## Table of Contents

# Nurturing Father

A man who actively provides guidance, love, and support to enhance the development and growth of children for whom he cares.

# WELCOME!
## To The Nurturing Father's Program

The Nurturing Father's Journal of

_____
(name)


The group will meet every_____
                                          (day)


between _____ at _____ for 13 weeks.
        (time)                   (place)


What I hope to get from this program:

_____
_____
_____
_____
_____
_____
_____
_____
_____
_____
_____

*When I see a father*
*walking across a field,*
*or sliding through a sandlot,*
*or catching the fly of a stream*

*I cannot forget what is impossible*
*for me to remember.*

– Martin Tucker
*The Presence of Absence*

*And that son had a father who became his whole*
*world. They learned from each other, laughed*
*with each other, argued with each other and*
*loved. The bond between fathers and sons is*
*unbreakable. It can be celebrated, cursed,*
*strained, ridiculed, and honored,*
*it cannot, however, be broken.*

– Bill Hanson
*Father & Son: The Bond*
A collection of photographs and essays

# Week 1

# The Roots of Fathering

# Program Objectives - Week 1

To introduce group members to the *Nurturing Father's Program.*

To share introductions by group members.

To clarify the relationship between our father's (or father figure's) and our own style of fathering.

# Fathering His-Story

I am the Father/Stepfather/Grandfather/Male Guardian/Mentor of:

Names and ages of children: _____.

My immediate family includes:_____.
spouse, others

Becoming a Father: (What circumstances/events led you to this place?)

_____
_____
_____
_____
_____
_____
_____

Births: (Describe your experiences, thoughts, and feelings around the birth of each of your children.)

_____
_____
_____
_____
_____
_____
_____

Transitions: (Divorce, death, remarriage, etc., and what resulted from these changes.)

_____
_____
_____
_____
_____
_____
_____

We learn how to be fathers from our fathers or father role models.

We tend to father the way
we were fathered.

There is a powerful link between
us and our fathers, which should be
acknowledged and respected.

Even if our father was absent, his absence is
part of who we are. There is an "invisible
bond" that links us to the absent father and
influences us as fathers.

But we are not condemned to
repeat our father's mistakes.

We can choose to be the father
we want to be.

# Visualization: My Father and Me

List all the qualities, descriptive words, and phrases that describe your father's (or primary father figure's) fathering style and relationship to you.

_____

_____

_____

_____

_____

_____

_____

_____

_____

_____

_____

_____

_____

_____

_____

If your father was absent, what did that leave you with – longings, hurt, determination to be different? What do you know about him from others?

_____

_____

_____

_____

_____

_____

_____

_____

_____

_____

_____

_____

"It's a bunch of stuff my dad gave me. I'm going to go through it and save some, throw some away, and add some of my own."

# Vision Statement:
# The Father I Choose to Be

*(Reference the visualization "My Father and Me" on page 5 and the cartoon "Boxes" on the opposite page)*

## Save Some:
*(List the specific aspects of your father's fathering style that you choose to adopt as your own.)*

I choose to:

_____

_____

_____

_____

_____

_____

## Throw Some Away:
*(List the specific aspects of your father's fathering style that you chose not to use.)*

I choose not to:

_____

_____

_____

_____

_____

_____

## Add Some of My Own:
*(List any additional fathering qualities that you choose to utilize.)*

In addition, I choose to:

_____

_____

_____

_____

_____

_____

# Letting Go

Read the following quietly. In fact, read the words several times. Feel free to change the wording to reflect your own individual thoughts.


Father . . .

I acknowledge who you are.

I see you clearly, your strengths and weaknesses,

and I accept those fathering ways that I choose to carry on as my own.

And, father . . . I need to let you go, to say good-bye;

So that I can be free, fully me, the father I am meant to be.


With these words you may feel sadness, anger, or other feelings. Be accepting, patient, and nurturing to yourself. These feelings represent the grief we feel as we separate from our own fathers in order to become our full selves (as men and as fathers).

# Fathers Come in Different Cultural Styles

Briefly describe the role and characteristics of the father in your cultural/ethnic group:

_____

_____

_____

_____

_____

_____

_____

_____

_____

_____

_____

_____

How does this cultural role influence you as a father?

_____

_____

_____

_____

_____

_____

_____

_____

_____

_____

_____

_____

# Notes:

# Home Activities: Week 1

**1.** Complete "The Father I Choose To Be" Vision Statement
*(page 7, A Nurturing Father's Journal).*

**2.** Bring in a memento from your father
*(a photo, letter, object, story, song, etc.).*

**3.** Consider your ethnic/cultural background *(e.g., African-American, Hispanic, Jewish, Irish, Japanese, Chinese, Hawaiian, American Indian, other)* and the role of the father in your culture. Complete "Fathers Come in Different Cultural Styles" *(page 9, A Nurturing Father's Journal).*

## Thought for the week:

Who our father was and how we felt as a child allow us as adults to make choices about our own fathering style.

*You were beside me.*
*You were the mountain*
*blocking half*
*a sky full of stars.*

*I was small*
*in the depth of your shadow*
*watching black water*
*and glittering boats.*

– William Pitt Root
from *Walking to the Comet*

*...so I pushed against the cycle –*
*poor, black, fatherless –*
*to see if it would break.*

– Mbembe Milton Smith
from *Ancestry as Reality*

# Week 2    Self-Nurturing Skills 1: Fathering The Little Boy Within

# Program Objectives - Week 2

To share visions of "The Father I Choose To Be."

To explore different cultural styles of fathering.

To learn to identify the "little boy" within each man/father.

To learn to establish a nurturing relationship (self-nurturing) with this little boy.

# My Little Boy Within

His name: _____

His nickname (if any): _____

Describe his feelings:

Ways I can nurturingly respond to his feelings:

_____
_____
_____
_____
_____
_____
_____
_____

Describe his needs:

Ways I can nurturingly respond to his needs:

_____
_____
_____
_____
_____
_____
_____
_____
_____

Please add anything else you know about this little boy and your relationship to him:

_____
_____
_____
_____
_____

Practice being "The Father I Choose To Be" to the little boy within. He needs and deserves a nurturing father.

## Our Unmet Needs from Childhood - "the Little Boy Within"

We have been discussing our father and his relationship (or lack of relationship) with us.

We were the child (the little boy) growing up.

As a child, none of us got all our needs met from our father or mother. Each of us has unmet needs - some more than others.

For example, if our father was absent, we may have needed more of his time and attention. If our father hit or yelled a lot, we may have needed kindness or protection. If our father criticized us, we would have liked to have heard "good job," "great effort." Perhaps we needed to hear "I love you."

These unmet needs are often still in us today, as if that little boy is still asking to be cared for and to have his needs met. The little boy that we were still lives within us and deserves to have his needs met.

But our fathers are not here to meet these needs.

We, as adults, can notice these unmet needs (the little boy within) and respond in a nurturing manner. Each of us can be a nurturing father to ourselves, to the unmet needs of the little boy within.

This will help us and make it easier to be a nurturing father to our children.

# Home Activities: Week 2

**1.** Complete "My Little Boy Within" *(page 15, A Nurturing Father's Journal).*

**2.** Re-read "The Father I Choose To Be" vision statement from Week 1. Practice being this father as you relate to your little boy within.

## Thoughts for the week:

The little boy that we were still lives within us and deserves to have his needs met.

As adults, we can notice the unmet needs of our little boy within and respond in a nurturing manner.

*He never phrased what he desired
and I am his son.*

– Robert Bly
from *My Father at Eighty-Five*

# **Week 3**  Self-Nurturing Skills II: The Power To Meet My Own Needs

# Program Objectives - Week 3

To identify principles and practices for meeting one's own needs.

To identify strategies for overcoming blocks to self-nurturance.

To formulate encouraging messages for meeting specific needs.

# All human beings (men, women, and children) have needs.

Some needs must be met in order to stay alive.

Examples:_____

Some needs simply feel good when they are met.

Examples:_____

Who is primarily responsible for meeting my needs?

_____

# PERSONAL POWER is <u>my ability to meet my own needs</u>.

Using my personal power to meet my own needs in a POSITIVE way is self-nurturing.

Examples:_____

_____

Using my personal power to meet my own needs in a NEGATIVE way is self-destructive.

Examples: _____

_____

# I have the power to choose.

Self-nurturing promotes health, vitality, and success.

Self-nurturing helps me to nurture others (meet the needs of my children, spouse, partner, etc.).

When my "cup is full," I can give to others.

When my "cup is empty," giving to others is difficult.

# A PLAN FOR MEETING

| NEEDS: | PHYSICAL | SOCIAL | EMOTIONAL |
|---|---|---|---|
|  |  |  |  |
| How I can meet these needs |  |  |  |
| How I block myself from meeting these needs |  |  |  |
| Specific strategies to overcome blocks |  |  |  |

# MY OWN NEEDS

| INTELLECTUAL | CREATIVE | SPIRITUAL | |
|---|---|---|---|
| | | | |
| | | | |
| | | | |
| | | | |

# Self-Talk: Discouraging and Encouraging Messages

Self-talk describes the statements we make or messages we send to ourself inside our heads. Some of these messages are encouraging and help us meet our needs. Some are discouraging and block us from meeting our needs. We can use self-talk to create encouraging messages or to change discouraging messages to encouraging ones.

1. Discouraging Message:
   (a discouraging statement, possibly from childhood, that I say to myself)

   _____

   Encouraging Message:
   (change the discouraging message to a positive, encouraging statement)

   _____

2. Discouraging Message:

   _____

   Encouraging Message:

   _____

3. Discouraging Message:

   _____

   Encouraging Message:

   _____

4. Add any other encouraging messages that you would like to hear:

   _____

   _____

   _____

   _____

# Home Activities: Week 3

**1.** Review "Self-Talk: Discouraging and Encouraging Messages"
*(page 24, A Nurturing Father's Journal).*

**2.** Complete "A Plan for Meeting My Own Needs"
*(page 22-23, A Nurturing Father's Journal).* Put this plan
into practice beginning this week.

## Thoughts for the week:

'Blocks' are the specific ways we
deny, avoid, or distance ourselves from
meeting our needs.

Repeating encouraging messages to
ourselves reinforces positive self-talk
and is one way we can nurture ourselves.

Can I see a falling tear,
and not feel my sorrow's share?
Can a father see his child
Weep, nor be with sorrow fill'd?

– William Blake
from *On Another's Sorrow*

# Week 4

# The World of Feelings and Male Nurturance

# Program Objectives - Week 4

To accept feelings as a normal aspect of human experience and to reflect on our ability to experience and express a wide range of feelings.

To identify guidelines for relating to other people's feelings in a nurturing way.

To define the nurturing characteristics that are shared by both fathers/males and mothers/females.

To identify the nurturing characteristics that exemplify the father/male style of parenting.

# Relating to My Feelings

This worksheet shows different feelings. Each feeling is represented by two bars:

    A.  FEEL: *How easy or difficult is it to feel or experience that feeling?*

    B.  EXPRESS: *How easy or difficult is it to express or show that feeling to others?*

Put a mark in each bar to show how easy or difficult it is to feel and to express the following feelings:

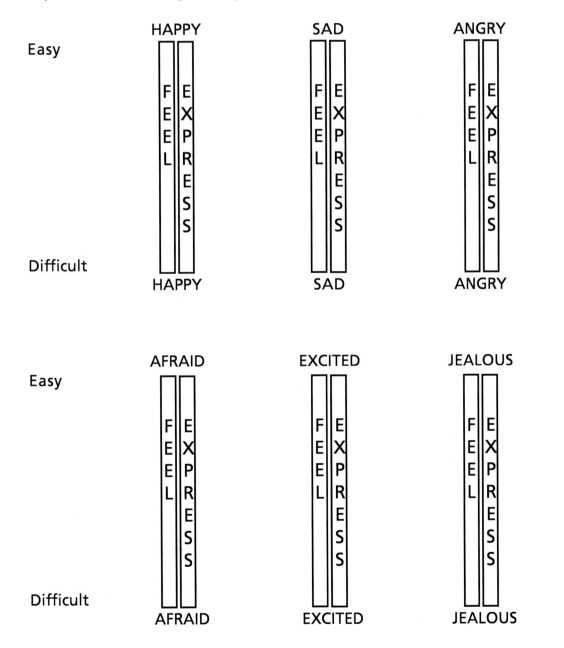

# My Feelings

Which feelings are the easiest . . .

    to feel? _____

    to express? _____

Which feelings are the most difficult . . .

    to feel? _____

    to express? _____

What I remember being taught about feelings:

_____

_____

_____

Are men taught different values regarding feelings than women?

    anger: _____

    sadness: _____

    fear: _____

    (other feelings): _____

What do I want my son(s)/daughter(s) to learn about feelings?

_____

_____

_____

Feelings and their appropriate expressions connect me to people and experiences.  They are part of the world of intimacy and nurturing.

# Relating to Others' Feelings

Do not deny or judge another person's feelings. Feelings come from deep within the self. To deny or criticize someone's feelings is to deny part of who they are.

Accept people's feelings. (Remember, you can help another person express or act out their feelings differently, without denying their feelings.)

Identify a feeling by its name. "Are you sad?" "You seem angry."

Help another person express their feelings (in ways that do not hurt themselves or others). Let them talk.

Let people display their feelings (e.g., crying). Ask the other person what they need.

Being with another person and their feelings is part of intimacy and nurturing fathering.

# The World of Male Nurturance

The following are characteristics of nurturing, and they are common to both males/fathers and females/mothers (add to the list):

Expressing love
Encouraging
Nonsexual touching (hugging)
Limit setting
Listening

_____
_____
_____
_____
_____

The following characteristics of nurturing tend to be more common to males/fathers (add to the list):

Focusing on doing

Emphasizing performance and competence

Encouraging risk taking

Focusing on boundaries/ rules/standards

Fostering independence

Focusing on justice/fairness

Role modeling maleness/ fathering

_____
_____
_____
_____
_____
_____
_____

The following characteristics of nurturing tend to be more common to females/mothers (add to the list):

Focusing on being

Emphasizing acceptance and safety

Protecting

Being emotionally attuned

Fostering relatedness

Being forgiving

Role modeling femaleness/ mothering

_____
_____
_____
_____
_____
_____
_____

All nurturing characteristics and practices are to be encouraged. And if we, as fathers, identify with some of the male nurturing qualities listed above . . . Honor and cultivate them!

Children love to please their father.

Your positive attention and recognition are a great gift to your son(s) and daughter(s).  They help to build self-esteem and self-confidence.

Give them your undivided attention.

Praise effort and attempts.

Notice progress and improvement.

Let them know you believe in them.

## AVOID:

Perfectionism: "Anything less than perfect isn't good enough."
(translates into "I'm not good enough")

Criticism: "You make too many mistakes."
(translates into "I can't")

# Fathering Practices

List the specific practices (tools) that a father can use in parenting children to encourage desired behaviors or change undesired behaviors. In the left column, list those that you consider to be "nurturing" practices. In the right column, list the "non-nurturing" practices.

| NURTURING | NON-NURTURING |
| --- | --- |
| | |
| | |
| | |
| | |
| | |
| | |
| | |
| | |
| | |
| | |
| | |
| | |
| | |
| | |
| | |
| | |
| | |

Put all of the fathering tools that you can think of on the list, whether or not you actually use them with your children.

# Home Activities:     Week 4

**1.**   Complete "My Feelings" *(page 30, A Nurturing Father's Journal).*


**2.**   Complete "Fathering Practices" *(page 34, A Nurturing Father's Journal)* for use in  group next week.


## Thoughts for the week:

Feelings, and their appropriate
   expressions, connect me to people
   and experiences.  They are part
   of the world of intimacy and
   nurturing.

Both men and women, boys and girls,
   have the capacity to feel and
   express the full range of feelings.
   It is part of being human.

*The child's lateness was not yet resistance to adult demands. He had merely forgotten time and would be reminded by the hands of his father who waited, so deep in his own story of terror and loss that even the angry beating of his heart was fear. When he saw the boy he joined the ends of his belt in his hand and rushed to join his child down the street before resistance on either part.*

– Jason Sommer
from *Joining the Story*

# Week 5

# The Power To Nurture: Fathering without Violence or Fear

# Program Objectives - Week 5

To differentiate between nurturing and non-nurturing fathering practices.

To identify the intentions and actual outcomes of various fathering practices.

To commit to the use of specific nurturing fathering practices that do not represent fear or violence.

To understand the differences between "power-over" and "power-to", and how they affect men's lives.

# The Challenge –

Can I lead without FEAR and VIOLENCE?  The choices (and outcomes) are mine!

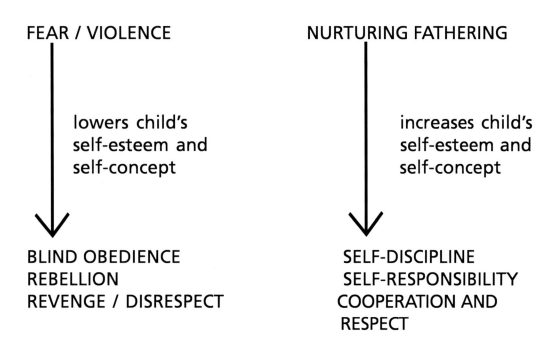

| FEAR / VIOLENCE | NURTURING FATHERING |
|---|---|
| lowers child's self-esteem and self-concept | increases child's self-esteem and self-concept |
| BLIND OBEDIENCE<br>REBELLION<br>REVENGE / DISRESPECT | SELF-DISCIPLINE<br>SELF-RESPONSIBILITY<br>COOPERATION AND RESPECT |
| Children Learn: Fear/Violence | Children Learn: Nurturing |

NOTE: ***Respect is something you must give in order to receive.***

# Intended Goals and Actual Outcomes

| Fathering Practices | Intended Goal (parent) |
| --- | --- |
| Hitting (corporal punishment) | Getting their attention. Stopping undesired behavior. Teaching discipline. Teaching respect. |
| Yelling | Getting their attention. Communicating something of importance. Teaching discipline and respect. |
| Put-Downs (criticism) | Attention to undesired behavior. Stopping undesired behavior. Teaching "what not to do." |
| Expressing Love | Instilling feelings of love and well-being. |
| Encouraging | Facilitating growth and development. Facilitating competence and performance. |
| Praise | Attention to desired behavior. Teaching "what to do." Showing parental approval. |
| Hugs | Nonsexual physical expression of love, tenderness. |
| Giving Choices | Empowerment. Learning to analyze and solve problems. |
| Consequences | Teaching discipline and responsibility. Discouraging undesirable behavior. |
| Listening | Learning about child's thoughts and feelings. Communicating interest and caring. |
| Family Rules | Setting limits. Balancing adult and child needs and desires. Learning what is "not OK" vs. "OK." |

Actual Outcome (child)

Gets their attention – they see anger/violence. Hurts physically and emotionally. Damages self-esteem. Teaches violence/power-over. Leads to revenge, fear.

Child turns off and shuts down; does not hear message. Hears anger, violence/power-over. Feels badly about self (lowers self-esteem). Leads to revenge, fear, disrespect.

Child feels hurt (lowers self-esteem). Undesired behavior gets attention. Doesn't teach "what to do." Leads to discouragement, withdrawal, resentment.

Feels love and lovable. Increases self-esteem, sense of well-being, and ability to express love to others.

Promotes will to succeed, to take risks, to grow, to learn. Increases ability to tolerate failure.

Increased self-esteem and self-concept. Tendency to repeat desired behavior. Sense of well-being, love, encouragement.

Feels loved, secure, safe. Increased self-esteem.

Feels empowered (power-to). Learns to analyze and solve problems. Leads to self-responsibility.

Learns self-discipline and self-responsibility.

Increased self-esteem. Sense of personal value and worth. Feels cared about and motivated to communicate with parent.

Learns limits and self-discipline. Practices respect and self-control.  Learns social skills.

# ACT . . . instead of **REACT**.

It is difficult to control
   how I feel,
   but I can CHOOSE
   how I ACT in response to feelings.

And my actions can be guided
   by nurturing fathering practices
   that lead to *desired outcomes.*

Turn to the following page to revise the list of your nurturing and non-nurturing  practices to reflect *your plan of action.*

# My Nurturing Fathering Practices

Plan of Action

These are the nurturing fathering practices that I choose to use for parenting my children:

_____

_____

_____

_____

_____

_____

_____

_____

_____

_____

_____

These are the non-nurturing fathering practices that I choose not to use:

_____

_____

_____

_____

_____

_____

(Refer to page 34, "Fathering Practices," and to page 40-41, "Intended Goals and Actual Outcomes.")

# Power-over vs. Power-to:
# styles of using power

All people want and deserve to be empowered, to feel powerful. But different "styles" of using power yield different results. One style of power can result in harm to others and to relationships while another can be helpful to others and to relationships.

The change from power-over to power-to is a central, pivotal concept in this program. If you choose to let it in, it can be transformational in becoming a nurturing father.

It can transform your relationship to yourself (your physical body and emotions), your children, your spouse, even to the world.

This issue of power appears here, at about the midpoint of this program – and it is central to all that comes before and after it.

Let's look more closely at the transformative potential of this simple notion....

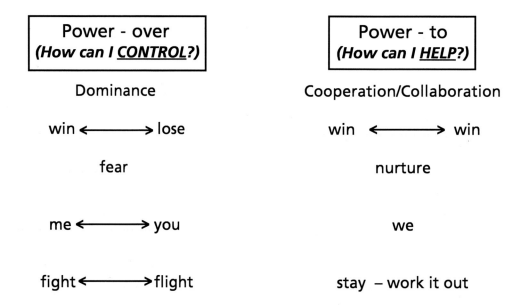

| Power - over (How can I *CONTROL*?) | Power - to (How can I *HELP*?) |
| --- | --- |
| Dominance | Cooperation/Collaboration |
| win ⟷ lose | win ⟷ win |
| fear | nurture |
| me ⟷ you | we |
| fight ⟷ flight | stay – work it out |

Let's take a closer look at how these different styles of power affect important aspects of our life.

# Changing Power-over to Power-to
# and How It Affects Mens' Lives

| | POWER-OVER results in... | POWER-TO results in... |
|---|---|---|
| The Little Boy Within | Denying his existence, controlling his expressions. Cannot acknowledge needs and ask for help. | Being open to his needs, messages, and longings. Can identify and provide for own needs and is able to ask others for help. |
| Physical Body | Blocking its subtle messages, becoming inflexible, out-of-touch. Denying needs and warning signs. | Being in touch with the body's rhythm and messages; able to respond and address the physical needs and warning signs. |
| Emotions | Controlling the "vulnerable" emotions (fear, sadness). Not feeling or expressing them. Anger as the primary vehicle for emotional release. Limited intimacy. | Feeling and understanding one's deeper emotional self and sharing this with others. Anger balanced with other emotions and expressed in nondestructive ways. Greater capacity for intimacy. |
| Children | Control, dominance, fear, distance, leading to rebellion. (This can result in physical abuse, rape, or sexual abuse.) | Respect, admiration, leading to relaxed relatedness, role-modeling, intimacy, empathy. |
| Spouse/Co-Parent/ Intimate Others | Power struggle, conflict, one-way communication, leading to fear, tension, attacking problems through win/lose. Distance from other people. | Cooperation, compromise, two-way communication, leading to relaxed relatedness, real teamwork, creative compromise and problem solving, intimacy. Closeness to other people. |
| Leadership | Control, dominance, isolation, "my way = right way," motivated by personal ego needs ("I"). Results in low productivity, low morale, low creativity and initiative. | Visionary, mission/goal-driven, collaboration and teamwork, mediates conflicts. Utilizes differences creatively. Motivated by benefit to the common good ("We"). Results in higher productivity, high morale, high creativity and initiative. |

INFLUENCE increases as the need to CONTROL decreases.

Therefore,

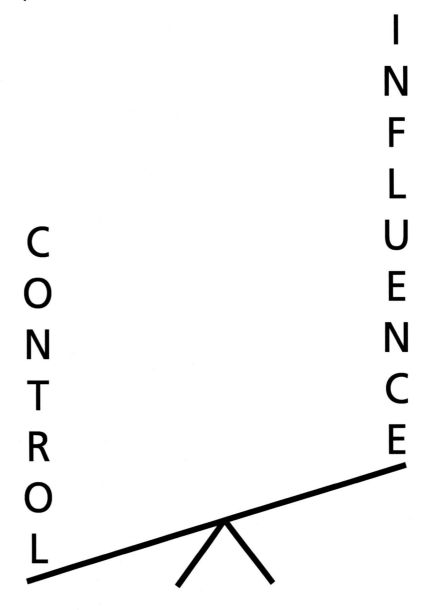

# Unconditional Love

This is love without conditions or judgments—no "ifs, ands, or buts."

It is the foundation for all other nurturing fathering practices.

List three ways in which you can express unconditional love to your children:

(e.g., "I am so glad that you are my son/daughter." "I always love you." "Yes, even when I don't like what you are doing at that moment.")

1._____

_____

2._____

_____

3._____

_____

Express these feelings often to your children and loved ones. This will build a foundation for loving relationships and will also be deeply reassuring.

# Notes:

# Home Activities:    Week 5

**1.** Read "Power-over vs. Power-to" *(page 44-46, A Nurturing Father's Journal)*.

**2.** Complete "My Nurturing Fathering Practices" (Plan of Action) *(page 43, A Nurturing Father's Journal)*

**3.** Complete "Unconditional Love" *(page 47, A Nurturing Father's Journal)* and say these words to your children this week.

**4.** Be patient with yourself and your child/ren. This is a learning process that takes time and patience. Bring any successes and failures to the next group meeting. We learn from **both!**

## Thoughts for the week:

All nurturing fathering practices have this in common: They accomplish their goal without using fear or violence.

Respect is something you must give in order to receive.

*I help him from his chair*
   *to the john. He pees slowly,*
   *fingers like hams*
   *on his fly, a complex*
   *test of logic*
   *for a man this drunk.*
   *I'm splashing cold water in his face*
   *and he tells me he's dying,*
   *"Don't say a thing to your mother,*
   *and please, Dave,*
   *don't ever remember me like this."*

                    – David Wojahn
                       from *Heaven For Railroad Men*

# Week 6

# Overcoming Barriers to Nurturing Fathering

# Program Objectives - Week 6

To recognize anger, alcohol/other substances, and stress as potential barriers to nurturing fathering.

To analyze the dynamics of anger and identify tools to manage it.

To understand the relationship between excessive anger and alcohol/other substances and to increase the awareness of group members' patterns of alcohol/substance use.

To practice stress-reduction techniques.

# Anger

Anger is a natural, normal emotion. It is not, in itself, a problem. But it can become a problem that can present an obstacle to nurturing fathering. When does anger become a problem?

- when it is so excessive that it *feels* out of control

- when we ACT from anger in a way that hurts others (or ourself)

Hitting, yelling, and insulting people, etc., are examples of anger hurting others. Understanding how anger works is an important first step in managing it.

Anger, as a powerful emotion, can feel "out of control." Even though it can be difficult to control how we feel, that does not mean that we are powerless. Feelings do not "make us do things." If we look closely at ANGER, we can see that

- something precedes it and

- something follows it.

FEELING
(anger)

THINKING                    ACTING

Anger is preceded by THINKING. In fact, certain thoughts are the fuel that we use to fire up anger. The more of these thoughts that we throw on to the fire, the hotter the feeling of anger becomes. Let's consider the following example:

Our two-and-a-half year old screeches "NO" and throws the toy on the ground. What thoughts can fuel anger here? How about "He is defiant," "She doesn't respect me," and "He'll grow up with no discipline?"

Our first tool for managing anger is to take a step back and look at the THOUGHTS that precede it, then change the thinking.

| inaccurate | to | → | accurate thoughts |
| negative | to | → | positive thoughts |
| non-nurturing | to | → | nurturing thoughts |

Look at the thoughts from the example on the previous page and change them to reflect a more accurate, nurturing vision of the two-and-a-half year-old's behavior. They might sound like this:

- "Kids that age say 'No' a lot."

- "Independent, but a little too strong."

- "Angry, but not a good way to express it by throwing things."

NOTE: This entire thinking process caused the father to STOP, PAUSE, and REFLECT. This is POSITIVE in itself. It gives us some distance from the ANGER (feeling), buys some time, and removes logs from the fire. (The anger can cool down.)

What follows the THINKING ➔ FEELING, is ACTING —taking action, doing something. We can *choose* an action that is NOT violent or destructive. The pausing and reflecting that was done in step 1 should make this next step easier. But, in any case, what we DO with our anger and the ENERGY surrounding it is within our control. (In fact, by using this process we maintain control over ourself and the situation, instead of reacting in a way that is out of control.)

In step 1, reflecting, pausing, and thinking decreased the anger. This allows for dealing directly with the child's behavior by using a nurturing fathering practice, e.g., choices and consequences. ("If you throw your toys, we'll have to put them away for awhile. But if you play without throwing them, then we'll leave them out.") But if the feeling of anger is still strong and can lead to violent action, then something must be DONE (action) with this ENERGY (anger).

Here are a few suggestions: walk away; take a time-out break to another room; ask co-parent or another adult to step in; run around the block; write down the angry thoughts and feelings; call a friend or a group member whom you've learned to trust; attack the problem (not the person), asking yourself, "What can I DO to change the situation?"; evaluate the consequences of different actions.

You can also help your child/ren deal with their anger by showing them how to use these techniques.

# Alcohol and Other Substances

What is the relationship between alcohol (or other substances) and anger?

> Alcohol decreases inhibitions and can release stored-up anger. Judgment is impaired, and the anger can result in actions that hurt others.

What is the relationship between alcohol and auto fatalities?

> Alcohol is a factor in at least 50% of all traffic deaths each year.

What do children learn when they observe their father drunk or using illegal substances?

> They learn that it's okay to get drunk or break the law.

How can excessive alcohol use or drugs cause harm to families?

> It leads to secrecy. It teaches victimization. It creates family dysfunction, which children replicate when they become parents. It can create serious personality disorders in children.

## IMPORTANT GUIDELINES:

- Do not use illegal drugs.

- If you drink alcohol, drink in moderation.
  *(moderation = no more than one to two drinks in a 24-hour period)*

(Information taken from *Nutrition and Your Health: Dietary Guidelines for Americans*, Third Edition, 1990, U.S. Department of Agriculture, U.S. Department of Health and Human Services.)

# Alcohol and Other Substances:

Families and Chemical Use Questionnaire
The following questions are designed to only increase your awareness about your chemical use and the chemical use of any family member. The word "chemical" in these questions refers to all mood altering substances such as alcohol, pot, speed, uppers, downers, etc. Answer the questions as honestly as you can. You will not be required to turn this questionnaire in to anyone.

## ABOUT YOU

|  | | Yes | No |
|---|---|---|---|
| 1. | Do you feel you have a chemical use (pot, alcohol, speed, downers, uppers, etc.) problem ? | ____ | ____ |
| 2. | Do you often use a chemical to feel better? | ____ | ____ |
| 3. | Do you often use a chemical to "get through the day"? | ____ | ____ |
| 4. | Do you spend more money on your chemical than you planned? | ____ | ____ |
| 5. | Do you feel annoyed or irritated if your family or friends discuss your chemical use? | ____ | ____ |
| 6. | Have you had any arguments with your family or friends because of your chemical use? | ____ | ____ |
| 7. | Have you ever failed to keep a promise you made to yourself about cutting down on your chemical use? | ____ | ____ |
| 8. | Do you tend to use your chemical at times when you feel angry, disappointed, depressed, anxious, or lonely? | ____ | ____ |
| 9. | Have you ever been careless of your family's welfare when you've been using a chemical? (Driving under the influence, falling asleep with a burning cigarette, not caring where your kids were, blowing a paycheck on chemicals, hitting a family member while under the influence?) | ____ | ____ |
| 10. | Do you use chemicals in the morning to help you recover from the night before? | ____ | ____ |

## ABOUT YOUR FAMILY

|  | | Yes | No |
|---|---|---|---|
| 1. | Do you feel a member of your family has a chemical use problem? | ____ | ____ |
| 2. | Do you lie awake worrying about your family member (of whatever age)? | ____ | ____ |
| 3. | Do you feel frustrated in your attempts to control your family member? | ____ | ____ |
| 4. | Do you argue with your family member about his/her use of chemicals? | ____ | ____ |
| 5. | Do you find it increasingly difficult to communicate with your family member? | ____ | ____ |
| 6. | Do you find yourself lying or covering up for your family member? | ____ | ____ |
| 7. | Do you feel resentful or hostile toward your family member? | ____ | ____ |
| 8. | Do you worry about your family member's behavior affecting other members of the family? | ____ | ____ |
| 9. | Has the family member been confronted about his/her use of chemicals? | ____ | ____ |
| 10. | Has the family member denied his/her use of chemicals? | ____ | ____ |

(used with permission from Dr. Stephen Bavolek, *The Nurturing Program for Parents and Children*)

# Stress

Stress can be simply explained as our instinctual response to real or imagined danger. The body and emotions prepare us for a protective response (fight or flight) that is healthy and normal. Then we return to rest.  But modern life is full of stresses (from work demands, finances, traffic jams, divorce, etc.) that can lead to long-term, chronic stress.  This can negatively affect one's health, emotional well-being, and relationships.

Chronic stress often reflects an imbalance in one's life that requires an adjustment.  The adjustment can often be making a simple change: (1) changing a situation such as cutting back on work, using time-management or problem-solving techniques, or altering habits or routines, etc., (2) changing an attitude such as expecting less, modifying goals, being less self-critical, or thinking more positively, etc.


## FOLLOWING ARE SUGGESTIONS FOR REDUCING STRESS:

Take time for yourself to meet your needs.  *(Refer to week 3, "Meeting My Own Needs." Paying attention to these needs is an excellent approach to stress management.)*

Prioritize essential tasks. Let non-essentials wait.

Exercise regularly.

Eat well.

Listen to your body *(do not deny the body's messages, such as pain or discomfort).* Get medical advice when needed.

Play and laugh.  Kids can help us do this.  *(The next two weeks of this program will focus on this area.)*

Conduct problem solving, finding new ways to address old problems.  *(see Week 10, "Teamwork between Father and Spouse")*

Practice relaxation exercises, such as the one experienced in group this week.  It will be helpful to find a quiet place and practice relaxation on a daily basis.

# Father Play:
# Fun & Games

List fun games or activities you recall playing as a child with your father/ father-figure and/or fun games/activities you currently play with your children.  For each game/activity indicate what made it fun.

| Fun games or activities: | What made it fun: |
| --- | --- |
|  |  |

# Home Activities: Week 6

**1.** Complete "Father Play: Fun & Games" *(page 58, A Nurturing Father's Journal).*

**2.** Read and review all of *A Nurturing Father's Journal* material through Week 6.

**3.** How is it going?  What successes, changes, and challenges are you noticing?

## Thought for the week:

Anger, alcohol or substance abuse, and excessive stress present obstacles to nurturing fathering by leaving little time, energy, focus, and patience for children and family.

*For the very true beginning of wisdom is the desire of discipline; and the care of discipline is love.*

Solomon 6:17

# Week 7

# Discipline and Fun & Games

# Program Objectives - Week 7

To learn the key to techniques for discipline and behavior management through an understanding of team sports.

To establish family rules for the whole family.

To establish guidelines for nurturing play and plan a Playshop for our children.

# Discipline and Team Sports

## 1. How "the game" is played

Most of you know something (perhaps a lot) about team sports, e.g., basketball, baseball, football, hockey, soccer, etc.

You may have played (or still do), watch, or have some familiarity with how a team sport is played.

If you understand how team sports work, you probably know more than you think you do about disciplining children.

As an example, let's take the sport of basketball. (You can use any of the aforementioned sports). Draw the basic court design.

In order to start playing, what does everybody have to know and understand about the game?

- The goal: to get the ball into the basket
- The lines and the rules: what they mean
- What to do to win
- The penalties (consequences) for breaking the rules

It is also important to remember:

To work together - teamwork

What one member does (good or bad) affects the whole team

Encourage the "good"

Discourage the "bad"

## 2.   Discipline

Discipline = teaching children to play by the rules so that they can be part of the team (family, school, society, etc.).

Let's take a closer look at how this analogy between team sports and discipline works.

FIRST, THE GOALS. Set up the playing field in a way that helps the child and family succeed (win). For example, if you have a toddler – and toddlers explore and get into things – move all fragile or valuable objects out of the child's reach. Put child-proof locks on cabinets where dangerous chemicals are stored. This is called "baby proofing" your home. It also helps you say "no" less frequently to the child, thus making life easier for the whole family.

An example for a teenager would be to remove all alcoholic drinks from your home or to keep them in a locked cabinet in order to discourage teenage drinking. Set up the playing field with the goals in mind.

Understand and explain the "game." For a family, the goals are to work together, to be safe and happy, to learn and grow, and to help each member get their needs met, without denying others. What one member does affects everyone (the whole team). Discipline is helping the child play by the rules so s/he will achieve the above goals.

SECOND, THE RULES. The rules must be clear and everyone must understand them. If there are no rules, or if the rules are not explained clearly, you cannot expect children to learn to play the game. (Note: It will be helpful if the children participate in creating the rules. This gives them more ownership and respect for the rules. As children get to be pre-teens and teens, this becomes essential.)

The rules apply to everyone.  Therefore, you and your child/ren (and spouse) will create family rules, e.g., "no hitting" applies to all family members; "put things away after you use them" applies to all family members; etc.

An explanation as to why the rule is important is helpful.

Rules have a "WHAT TO DO" for every "WHAT NOT TO DO".

Rules have two parts: Do's (what to do) and Don'ts (what not to do).

EXAMPLES:

| Do's (What To Do) | Don'ts (What Not To Do) |
|---|---|
| Play within the lines | Don't step outside the lines |
| Play hard/be safe | No hitting or hurting |
| Speak in a calm voice | No yelling or cursing |

### THIRD, ENCOURAGE TEAMWORK AND DESIRED BEHAVIOR.
What do team players do every time one player makes a foul shot, makes a good pass (assist), scores a goal/touchdown, etc? They give them a pat on the back, high five, compliment, etc. Every time!

There must be some special value in encouragement. What you pay attention to you are likely to see more of. Encourage, praise, and reward the behaviors that you want to see more of, i.e., the "what to do" list.

### Examples of Ways to Encourage Desired Behavior:

Praise - "well done," "good job," etc.

Encouragement - "great effort," "good try," "thanks for . . ."

Positive Touch - hug, pat on the back, high five, etc.

Expanded Privileges - more time to play, more mature activities, more of what the child values/desires, etc.

Rewards - objects, money.

Pay attention to the positive. This will have a powerful effect on shaping and encouraging the desired behavior (playing by the rules).

**FOURTH, DISCOURAGE MISBEHAVIOR.** Establish clear consequences for breaking the rules. If the consequences can be logically related to the transgression, then the child will learn more from the consequences. When a rule is broken, begin with a warning/reminder. State the "what not to do" and the "what to do."

The warning/reminder is stated as a choice followed by a consequence. It would sound something like this:

"If you stop yelling (what to do), then you can keep playing the game. If you continue yelling (what not to do), then you'll take a five-minute time-out. It's your choice." Such choices and consequences teach discipline and self-responsible behavior. There is an undesirable penalty/ consequence for misbehavior.

If the misbehavior occurs again, follow through with the consequence. Consistency is very important. (Note: Anger and violence are not part of the game. The referee never uses anger or violence to enforce the rules in team sports.)

EXAMPLES OF CONSEQUENCES (for discouraging misbehavior):

TIME-OUT (sit on the sidelines). "If you can't play by the rules, then you'll have to sit out for a while." The time-out should be brief, two to ten minutes depending on age.

BEING GROUNDED (big infraction; you miss a game). "If you get into a fight at school (what not to do), then you will stay home after school and not play with your friends. If you do not get into any fights (what to do), then you can go out and play."

LOSS OF PRIVILEGE (can't be on the starting team). "If you do not put your toys away when you're finished playing (what not to do), then you cannot play with them after your nap. But if you put them away (what to do), you can play with them later."

RESTITUTION (fines, payback). Pay for or replace what was lost or broken. Provide a service for breaking the rules. "If you take your sister's music tape without asking (what not to do), then you'll have to let her keep one of your tapes. Or ask her if you can borrow a tape (what to do). Then it's no problem."

That's the game plan. The family is a team, with parent(s) as both coach and referee. *Discipline is helping your child/ren become a team player and to learn to play by the rules.*

# Family Rules

Set up a time with all family members to create family rules using the following format.

| DO's (what to do) | DON'Ts (what not to do) | CONSEQUENCES (if . . . then . . .) |
| --- | --- | --- |
|  |  |  |

# Examples of Family Rules

| AGE | DO's | DON'Ts | CONSEQUENCES |
|---|---|---|---|
| Toddler | Put all toys, games, and other things away when you are finished using them. | Don't leave toys, games, and other things out after you are finished using them. | If you leave toys, games or other things out after you are finished using them, then you cannot use them for one day. |
| Early School Age | Speak in a clear, calm voice. | No yelling or cursing. | If you yell or curse, you go to time-out for five minutes. |
| Teen | Be home at agreed upon time or call if you will be late. | Don't come home later than agreed upon without calling first. | If you come home late without calling first, then you will come home one hour earlier tomorrow for each 30 minutes you were late. |

# Fun & Games
## GUIDELINES FOR NURTURING PLAY

Nobody gets physically hurt.  Safety comes first!

No one gets emotionally hurt.  Avoid criticism and put-downs.

Everyone is encouraged to PARTICIPATE.

Reward effort, not perfection (build self-esteem and confidence).

Minimize teaching and instruction.

Lead with encouragement and modeling.

It's okay to give and receive help.

Encourage teamwork and cooperation.

The goal is . . . FUN!

Dads, let your "little boy" out to PLAY.

(Also, make adjustments according to age, size, and skill level.  If the child and the game don't fit, change the game.)


## A SUGGESTED PLAYSHOP FORMAT

(1 Hour)     Four play areas, each with a different fun game or activity, e.g.,bowling, ball in the basket, ring on the bottle. Be creative and draw from your childhood.

Children form four small groups and spend 15 minutes at each activity/play station, then move on to the next activity/play station for 15 minutes until each group has done all four activities/play stations.

(15 min.)     Fun Snacks - all together

(15 min.)     Songs - all together

(30 min.)     Stories -  all together (either read, told, or acted)

End:          Group Hug - all together



NOTE: *Older teens can help organize play stations and assist the younger children.*

# Notes:

# Home Activities:    Week 7

**1.** Read the section entitled "Discipline and Team Sports" *(pages 63-66, A Nurturing Father's Journal.)*

**2.** Set aside time this week with all family members to discuss and complete "Family Rules" *(page 67, A Nurturing Father's Journal).*

**3.** Preparation for Playshop: Bring any games, toys, materials, food, songs, stories, etc., for the Playshop next week.

DON'T FORGET: BRING YOUR CHILD/REN!

## Thoughts for the week:

Discipline is teaching children
   to play by the rules so they can
   be part of the team.

Pay attention to positive behaviors.
   What you pay attention to, you
   are likely to see more of.

You are the bows from which
your children as living arrows
are sent forth.

– Kahil Gibran
from *The Prophet*

# Week 8

# Playshop: Fun & Games for Fathers and Their Children

## Program Objectives - Week 8

To experience a Playshop with our child/ren.

To assess the value of the Playshop experience.

# Observations and Reflections on the Playshop Experience

What I enjoyed most:

_____

_____

_____

_____

_____

_____

What my children enjoyed most:

_____

_____

_____

_____

_____

_____

What I learned from the experience:

_____

_____

_____

_____

_____

_____

_____

_____

_____

# Notes:

# Home Activities:    Week 8

Complete "Observations and Reflections on the Playshop Experience"
*(page 75, A Nurturing Father's Journal).*

## Thought for the week:

Researchers have observed that many
fathers engage in physical play to
challenge and stimulate their child.
This type of father-child interaction
can influence a child's ability to
manage frustration, explore new
activities, and solve problems in
creative ways.

*And that son had a father who became his whole world. They learned from each other, laughed with each other, argued with each other and loved. The bond between fathers and sons is unbreakable. It can be celebrated, cursed, strained, ridiculed, and honored, it cannot, however, be broken.*

– Bill Hanson
from *Father & Son: The Bond*
A collection of photographs
and essays.

*How will you know*
*how much I love you?*
*You who are now*
*an unopened leaf in a bud this cold March...*

– Vance Crummett
from *To My Daughter*

# Week 9

# Nurturing Relationships I: Fathering Sons/ Fathering Daughters

# Program Objectives - Week 9

To discuss the Playshop experience with other group members.

To practice the communication skills of active listening and reflecting.

To explore the unique roles of fathering daughters and fathering sons.

To learn strategies for teaching values to children.

# Communication Skills:
# Guidelines for Active Listening and Reflecting
(Perlman, *Group Process and Teamwork,* 1986)

Nurturing, respectful communication is a two-way process:

> A) SENDING - speaking clearly and succinctly, in language easily understood by the child (or other person).

> Reminder: We communicate facts as well as feelings, and we communicate with body language and tone of voice, as well as with words.

> B) RECEIVING - listening actively and empathetically by using the following guidelines:

Listen with a clear and open mind.  This is a *receptive* process.  Common barriers to active listening are: being preoccupied or distracted; judging and evaluating; anger; formulating responses or arguments; interrupting.

Listen for content (facts, story line) as well as for feelings.

Listen deeply for the meaning underlying the words.

Empathize. Try to put yourself in the child's position or experience.

Look for nonverbal cues, e.g., body language, facial expression, etc.


Then, ***reflect back*** on what you heard:

> Restate the Content  -  paraphrase the facts; story line
>
> and
>
> Link with the Feeling - ***"And you feel _____."***

# Examples:

1. Child says: *"I hate that teacher for giving me a D. She's dumb."*

   Father responds: *"Your teacher gave you a D, and you feel angry at her."*

   > Reminder: Reflecting back feelings is often our "best guess" from what the child is showing us. Allow the child to confirm or correct our impression.

2. Child says: *"Two days before the dance and he finally asked me. I almost gave up hope!"*

   Father responds: *"Oh, he finally asked you to the dance, and you feel relieved and happy."*

   Child's inner reaction: *"Dad, you really understand me."*

   > This leads to increased openness, trust, and rapport between father and child. It also encourages feelings of self-worth and self-esteem within the child. Thus, the communication channel is kept open. This is a vital asset, especially when children become teenagers.

# Fathering Sons/Fathering Daughters

Active, warm, and nurturing attention from the father, from the earliest possible stage of development (pregnancy, birth, or infancy), creates appropriate bonding and attachment between father and child. This bond forms the foundation for a positive relationship. It eases the strains that often develop during certain stages and transitions, such as pre-adolescence and adolescence. Overall, a caring, nurturing, and involved father will have the most positive influence on his children.

Core message (for all ages and stages of development):

**_"You are lovable and capable."_**

Children grow from   DEPENDENCE    to    INDEPENDENCE.
         (reliance on others)        (self-reliance)

I can allow and actively support this process by viewing each child as a SELF, an independent person evolving and growing:

- in some ways, like me

- in other ways, different from me

I honor my child as a separate self, needing my guidance, love, protection, and nurturance in order to grow, just like a flower opening to full bloom, becoming all it is capable of being.

Observe yourself fathering
    through the eyes of your son . . .
    Be the father and the man
    you would like him to become.

Observe yourself fathering
    through the eyes of your daughter . . .
    Be the father and the kind of man
    you would like her to marry.

# Role Modeling

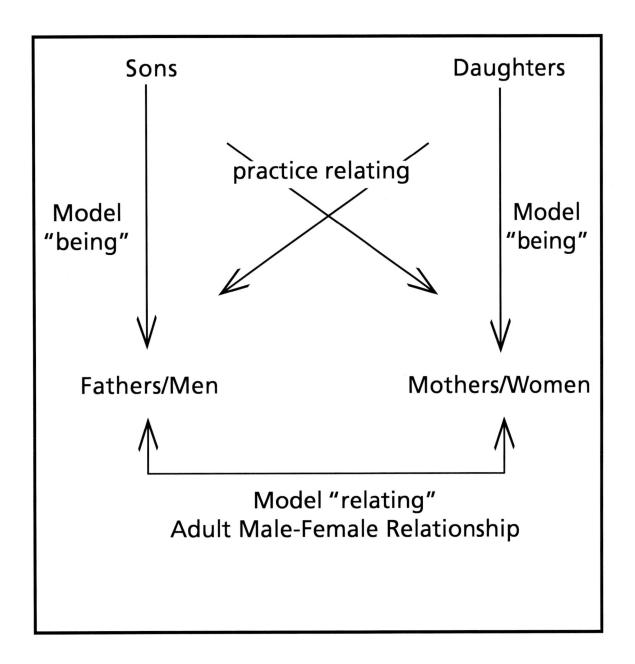

# Things To Consider When Fathering Daughters

Read and complete each item:

I must understand the feminine/female ways of being. (If I am not open to
understanding them, I may fear them, criticize them, or reject them. This will
hurt my ability to relate to my daughter.) Ask the women in your life to help
you understand the feminine ways. What did you learn from them?

_____

_____

_____

Even as a male and identifying with the masculine, I have some feminine
qualities. This is normal and healthy. Each of us, both male and female,
has a unique mix of these human characteristics, e.g., vulnerable feelings,
empathy, tenderness, nurturance, strength, etc. I can identify the following feminine aspects of myself:

_____

_____

_____

I actively support and nurture the feminine (developing woman) in my
daughter. I do this by:

_____

_____

_____

I acknowledge that my daughter comes into the world as a separate self,
with a wide range of potential. I support all she aspires to be, e.g., a
doctor, mother, athlete, businesswoman, etc. My daughter's current interests and abilities are:

_____

_____

_____

Boundaries are an important issue between father and daughter. They shouldn't be too close, such as too controlling, overprotective, or romantic/sexual, etc. Nor should they be too distant, such as physically removed/out of touch, emotionally removed/out of touch, etc. Do I need to adjust my boundaries with my daughter? If so, how? (If in doubt, ask the group for input.)

_____

_____

_____

My daughter will likely try out some of her maturing relationship skills with me, especially in her preteen or teen years. She might act flirty or seductive. I will maintain clear boundaries by (1) not rejecting her, and (2) not mistaking her actions for a romantic or sexual invitation. I will maintain this boundary by (if this is difficult, discuss it in group):

_____

_____

_____

My daughter will establish her identity and independence. She will challenge me (especially during her teen years). This type of behavior is normal and natural. I will try not to take it personally and become controlling. My daughter challenges me by:

_____

_____

_____

Prepare to LET GO. This is part of the fathering role. As my daughter becomes more responsible, I give her additional freedom. I can foster her independence by:

_____

_____

_____

# Things to Consider When Fathering Sons

Read and complete each item:

My son is learning from me how to be a man and to be a father.
  What I show him (behavior) is more influential than what I say (words).
  I am showing my son. . . .

_____

_____

_____

It is important to allow vulnerable and sensitive feelings to show and accept
  them in my son (e.g., "It's okay to cry," "Everyone feels afraid sometimes,"
  "I make mistakes, too.")  This is a sign of strength. I can do this by. . . .

_____

_____

_____

My son will imitate me and reflect a portion of who I am.  We are alike in
  the following ways:

_____

_____

_____

My son will be different from me, for he is a separate person with his own
  identity.  He is different from me in the following ways:

_____

_____

_____

Promoting independence and self-responsibility are the goals of parenting. (I will work myself out of a job). Signs of my son's growing independence are:

_____

_____

_____

I may have some unfulfilled dreams. If I try to live them through my son, I will burden him and our relationship. Areas where I might be pushing him are:

_____

_____

_____

My son will challenge me (especially during the teen years). This is natural and normal, and I do not want to crush his spirit. My son challenges me now by:

_____

_____

_____

Prepare to LET GO. This is part of the fathering role. As my son becomes more responsible, I give him more freedom. I can foster his independence by:

_____

_____

_____

# Teaching Values and Encouraging Value-Based Behavior

Role Model.  Children learn more from what we DO (behavior, actions) than from what we say. Lecturing and moralizing are ineffective tools for teaching values.  Practice/model the values that you want your children to learn. Live the values that you hope to pass on.

Affinity Groups.  Starting at an early age, involve the child in groups that reflect the values that are important to you and your family.  These groups can be religious, athletic, educational, social, artistic, skill building, etc. Children learn form the psychosocial environment as well as from positive peer contact.

Perform research and provide accurate information on specific topics, e.g., safe driving, drugs and alcohol, race and gender issues, sexual issues, etc. Ask children what they think about a subject. (We are often surprised by what they know.)

Use active listening skills to keep communication channels open.  Communication is a primary link to teens.  If we push them away and close off this channel, we will lose a vital source of influence.  Stay open and approachable as a parent.

Rituals.  Create rites of passage as well as celebrations to mark important events or accomplishments.  Weave values into these important moments. For example, celebrate your son's coming into manhood at age 13 by arranging a men's circle where songs, stories, and messages are shared. Or, for your daughter, celebrate an educational or athletic accomplishment by having a special ceremony.  You can also mark a child's graduation or leaving home with a ceremony that expresses your admiration and good wishes.

Family rules.   Establish rules with your children that reflect family values. It is important to include older children, especially teenagers, in the practice of formulating rules and the consequences for breaking the rules, e.g., "We do not hit or yell in this family," "We keep our commitments in this family," etc.

Praise.  Encourage your child and praise what s/he says or does that reflects the values you desire to instill. (If this is difficult, discuss it in group.)  The more you pay attention to these desired behaviors, the more likely the child will be to repeat them.

# Home Activities: Week 9

**1.** Practice the "Active Listening and Reflecting" style of communication *(page 81, A Nurturing Father's Journal)* with your children (and spouse, partner or others). Observe the results.

 Reminder: Be <u>patient</u> with yourself and with your family members. Change takes time.

**2.** Read and complete "Things To Consider When Fathering Sons" *(page 88-89, A Nurturing Father's Journal)* and "Things To Consider When Fathering Daughters" *(page 86-87, A Nurturing Father's Journal)* for your male and/or female children.

**3.** Write a specific conflict or problem that you are currently experiencing with your child/ren and/or partner.  You will have the opportunity to work on it at the next group meeting.

## Thought for the week:

In terms of relationship building,
 <u>how</u> we communicate (our style)
 is more important than
 <u>what</u> we communicate (the content).

*Two stonecutters were asked what they were doing. The first said, "I'm cutting this stone into blocks."*

*The second replied, "I'm on a team that's building a cathedral."*

Anonymous

# Week 10

# Nurturing Relationships II: Teamwork between Father and Spouse/ Co-Parent

# Program Objectives - Week 10

To identify the elements of successful teamwork and apply them to co-parenting with spouse/partner.

To learn and practice the skills of negotiation, conflict resolution, and cooperative problem solving.

To practice utilizing a method for dividing household/parenting tasks.

To discuss special issues in fathering, e.g., divorce, stepfathering, single fathering, and grandfathering.

# Teamwork between Father and Co-Parent (Spouse/Partner)

By cultivating love and mutual respect with a spouse/partner, we provide our children with a loving atmosphere as well as an example of a loving relationship. Nurturing the marital relationship is good for children as well as the family.

## Support

I will support my spouse/partner to be the best mother she can be.

I accept my spouse's/partner's support to help me be the best father I can be.

## Teamwork

My spouse/partner and I will co-parent together as a team for the best interest of our child(ren) and family.  We are the leaders of the family, and our relationship is the foundation of the family.

NOTE: Respect, support, and teamwork are no less important for separated or divorced couples.  Efforts to ease conflict and anger and to build a co-parenting relationship are very important for the well-being of the children.

Making an effort to accomplish this is an extension of nurturing fathering.

# Characteristics of Effective Teamwork

Successful teams have the following characteristics, whether they are on the sports field or at work:

- good communication
- trust
- reliability
- clear roles and rules
- mutual respect
- support
- cooperation
- loyalty
- acknowledgment of strengths and weaknesses
- leadership
- game plan

Spouses/partners are a team.

Cultivating the above qualities challenges us to grow individually and together, and we pass these qualities on to our children. Children learn about relationships by watching how father and mother/partner relate to each other.

# Co-Parenting as Teamwork

In a co-parenting relationship, both father and mother/partner should
expect their parenting styles to be different in some ways.
These differences are important to children, and they stimulate growth
and development in them.

Fathers should be careful not to criticize their partner's style of interacting
with the children, just as mothers should avoid any tendency to criticize or
belittle the father's style of parenting. Deep and sensitive personal and
gender issues come into play here, and they can lead to competition or
conflict.  Here are some important suggestions:

- Start sharing all parenting responsibilities early

- Expect the father's and mother's styles of interacting with children
  to  be different in some areas

- See these differences as positive for child development, and be
  respectful of them

- <u>Take a parenting class together</u>. This is a positive activity that
  will produce growth and also strengthen the co-parenting bond.
  It will also help define common ground for important issues, such
  as discipline, family rules, etc.

- Above all, practice *mutual respect, support,* and *cooperation.*

# Fathers of Newborns

Start early! Fathers of newborns should involve themselves in all parenting activities from the beginning.  This helps to develop skills and confidence in parenting, along with early bonding and attachment to their children.  Additionally, it establishes a more balanced co-parenting relationship between father and mother.

# Suggested Method for Dividing Household/ Parenting Tasks and Responsibilities:

1.   List all the tasks and responsibilities.

2.   Each partner should choose the ones s/he likes doing, prefers doing, is good at, etc.

3.   For dividing the remaining tasks and responsibilities (the grunt work, so to speak), use the negotiation, compromise, and problem-solving skills that will be discussed later in this chapter.

Note:  Ideally, a 50/50 split is desirable, all other things being equal. Each family needs to custom fit this process into its unique situation (e.g., percentage of time that either or both parents work; ages and needs of the children; special considerations, etc.).

4.   Involve the children in these household tasks (according to their age and abilities).  They should participate as part of the family team so they will learn those invaluable negotiation, compromise, and prob lem-solving skills.

5.   Write down the final agreement and date it.  Revise the plan as the needs and circumstances require, using the same process.

6.   Post the agreement in a visible place, such as on the refrigerator, where all family members can see it.

# Negotiation and Conflict Resolution

Most conflicts (and arguments) arise from a certain *style* of thinking and reacting (derived from a power-over style).

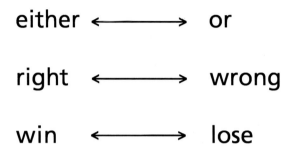

either ←——→ or

right ←——→ wrong

win ←——→ lose

Successful negotiation and conflict resolution require a change in this style of thinking to the following:

win ←——→ win

and ←——→ both

This is an attempt to incorporate <u>both</u> parties'/spouses' <u>interests</u> and <u>needs</u> into an outcome that they both can accept (or at least live with) instead of having one person defeat the other. The key question for this second type of thinking is: ***"What is your interest or need?"*** Once the interests or needs of both parties are identified, then a creative solution is possible.

# Example #1:

The conflict:

      Person 1:     **"I want to go bowling tonight."**

      Person 2:     **"No, I want to invite the Joneses over for dinner."**

Interest/Need:

      Person 1:     **"I've been sitting all day, and I need to do something active."**

      Person 2:     **"I'm interested in being with friends."**

Possible Resolutions:

**"Might we invite the Joneses to go bowling with us and then get a bite to eat afterward?"**

**"Maybe we could invite some friends to play volleyball in the back yard, then order food to be delivered."**

# Example #2:

The conflict:

      Person 1:     **"I'm tired of always visiting your parents on holidays."**

      Person 2:     **"My parents have no other family near them, and you don't seem to care."**

Interest/Need:

      Person 1:     **"I only have four days off, and I really need to do something fun just for us."**

      Person 2:     **"Being close to my parents on holidays is important to me."**

Possible Resolutions:

**"Maybe we can join my folks for a holiday dinner, then just you and I will drive up to the mountains and go for a hike."**

# Cooperative Problem Solving Model

Use the following five steps to address a problem between family members that they need to resolve together (teamwork in action).

## Examples of Problems:

"We have the house repair and a vacation planned, however with the doctor's bill due, we don't have enough money to do both."

"Jason just got his second D in algebra. What are we going to do?"

"The company is closing the local office and asking me to relocate, but your job and the kids' school are here."

## Five-Step Cooperative Problem Solving:

1.  Define the problem and discuss the facts. Share information and perceptions. See what's been tried and how it worked. Decide where you want to be/what the goal is.

2.  Brainstorm for alternative solutions. Allow for creative and expansive airing of possible solutions. Consider all alternatives. Do not judge, criticize, or evaluate.

3.  Prioritize the alternatives and choose a solution. Use reality testing, considering strengths, risks, and possible outcomes. Combine ideas and look for positive elements. Listen. Respect. Negotiate. Work toward a creative compromise.

4.  Put the plan into action. Be clear on expectations, roles, and responsibilities.

5.  Evaluation/Feedback. After the plan is in place, get back together to discuss how it's working. See if any revisions are needed. (If the plan has failed, return to step one and work through the process again and develop another solution).

(Perlman, *Group Process and Teamwork,* 1986)

# Home Activities: Week 10

**1.** Read the sections on teamwork and co-parenting *(pages 95-98, A Nurturing Father's Journal).*

**2.** Read and complete the activity on dividing household/parenting tasks and responsibilities *(page 99, A Nurturing Father's Journal).*

Thought for the week:

Working cooperatively as
a team/family encourages
us to grow individually
as well as together.

*We make a living by what we get,
but we make a life by what we give.*

– Norman MacEwan

# Week 11

# A Time and Place for Fathering

# Program Objectives - Week 11

To assess members' progress and utilize the program tools to assist with problem resolution.

To explore the relationships between time, work, and fathering.

To create a fathering job description that provides the required amount of time for carrying out the important duties and activities.

# Commitment

I am the father of

_____.

(names of children)

_____ is my son.
Name

_____ is my daughter.
Name

Fathering _____

(names of children)

is one of the most important jobs I have.

## I will make time for it.

## I am committed to doing the best job I can!

# A Bridge between Work and Fathering

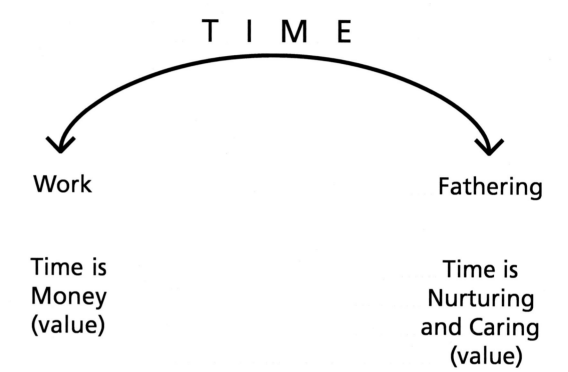

# Important Fathering "Times":

- Childbirth.  Be there with your spouse and newborn.

- Spend time with your spouse and bond with your baby.

- Attend parent/teacher conferences and open houses.

- Go to your child's athletic and cultural activities.

- Stay home with a sick child.

- Bring your child to work and show him/her what you do.

- Help with homework and projects.

- Play.

- Share in mundane tasks, such as changing diapers and doing housework.

# Additional Considerations Regarding Work and Fathering

Your work can have a profound influence on the quality of your fathering, well beyond the obvious factor of how it limits your time. Being overly involved in your career can result in the classic "absentee" father who has little time for his family and fathering. Preoccupation with work, however, can have a more subtle, but equally powerful, effect on your ability to be a nurturing father. For example, it can result in:

- Lack of physical energy and availability: "I would like to, but I'm too tired"

- Lack of emotional energy and availability; physically here but emotionally somewhere else

- Increased frustration and having a short temper, often expressed by yelling and hitting: "One more thing, and I'll . . ."

- Dictatorial style/high control needs: "Why can't I run my family like I run my shop?" (organization, business, crew, etc.)

- Little or no training to face the challenges at home (while there's sufficient training to handle the challenges at work): "Work problems I can fix; home/kid problems are much tougher"

- Need to feel in control at home due to having little control or autonomy at work: "I'm tired of being told what to do. It's time for me to tell someone what to do"

Be conscious of how work can affect the quality of your fathering.

# My Fathering Job Description

The following duties, responsibilities, and activities, plus the time each one requires, represent my fathering job description. The job of being the best father I can be demands that I attend to these responsibilities. I will evaluate my job performance on how well I carry them out.

| Duty, Responsibility, Activity | Time |
| --- | --- |
|  |  |
|  |  |
|  |  |
|  |  |
|  |  |
|  |  |
|  |  |
|  |  |
|  |  |
|  |  |
|  |  |
|  |  |
|  |  |
|  |  |
|  |  |
|  |  |
|  |  |
|  |  |
|  |  |
|  |  |
|  |  |

# The Joys of Fathering

List below those things you enjoy most about being a father:

Examples:     the things you love to do with your child/ren
              the funniest moments
              the most touching moments
              times you'll always remember

_____

_____

_____

_____

_____

_____

_____

_____

_____

_____

_____

_____

_____

_____

_____

_____

_____

_____

_____

_____

_____

# Home Activities: Week 11

**1.** Re-read "Commitment" *(page 107, A Nurturing Father's Journal)* and "My Fathering Job Description" *(page 111, A Nurturing Father's Journal)*.

Refer to these often during the coming week as you balance work, available time, and fathering.

**2.** Complete the activity titled "The Joys of Fathering" *(page 112, A Nurturing Father's Journal)*.

## Thought for the week:

Time is of value.
    Those things I value deserve my time.
    My child/ren are of value.
    I will give time to my child/ren.

*I think of your swallowed angers,*
*The pain on your face when I twisted grammar.*
*All your life you wrestled with fears that would*
*not become angels;*
*Inside your crabbed masculinity, was a*
*motherly sweetness*
*You could let out only when you were alone,*
*With the damp sand under your feet,*
*The foaming waves beside you.*
*With an artistry I still marvel at,*
*You remade yourself in that lonely space,*
*As you have remade yourself in me.*

– Paul Zweig
from *Father*

# Week 12

# Healing the Father Wound

# Program Objectives - Week 12

To reflect upon the special joys of fathering.

To reflect upon the things we would like to have heard from our father.

To experience receiving nurturing fathering messages.

To choose the messages we would like our child/ren to hear from us.

# The Things I Needed To Hear

Write below the things you most deeply needed to hear from your father - the words, phrases or statements that would have made you feel wonderful, valued, loved, capable, special.... the things that would have spoken to your deepest needs.

(Write the things you actually heard that made you feel this way or the things you wish you had heard.)

The things I most needed to hear from my father are:

_____

_____

_____

_____

_____

_____

_____

_____

_____

_____

_____

_____

_____

_____

_____

_____

_____

_____

_____

_____

_____

_____

# The Things I Need To Say

Write the most important nurturing messages that you need to say to your child/ren.  Write each exactly as you plan to say it.

(Note: If you have more than one child, be sure to write messages that speak directly to the needs of each one.)

The most important nurturing messages that I need to say to my child/ren are:

_____

_____

_____

_____

_____

_____

_____

_____

_____

_____

_____

_____

_____

_____

_____

_____

_____

_____

_____

_____

_____

_____

# Home Activities:    Week 12

**1.** Next week is our last Nurturing Father's group meeting. It will be a special graduation celebration to which child/ren, spouse, partner or other family members are invited for the first hour. Extend a special invitation to each person!

**2.** Complete "Commitment To My Family: The Father I Choose To Be (Revisited)" *(page 124, A Nurturing Father's Journal)* and bring it to the last group meeting.

**3.** Bring special food, snacks, drinks, or decorations to add to the celebration.

## Thought for the week:

Identifying aspects of our "father wound" and sharing healing experiences with other men frees us to be the nurturing father that each one of us is capable of being.

*He has achieved success
who has lived well,
laughed often
and loved much*

– Bessie Anderson Stanley

# **Week 13**  Graduation Ceremony and Closing Activity

# Program Objectives - Week 13

To review the goals and purpose of the *Nurturing Father's Program.*

To have each group member read his commitment to his family.

To celebrate and experience closure by giving and receiving feedback with other group members.

# Graduation

Congratulations! You have completed the **Nurturing Father's Program**. Although the program is ending, nurturing fathering continues. Take time to review this *Nurturing Father's Journal,* and note the growth you have achieved during the past twelve weeks.

---

### Format  –  Graduation Ceremony

Children, spouse/partner and family members attend for the first hour.

- Welcome and introductions

- 1 hour: Group members read "The Father I Choose To Be" and receive their graduation certificate

- Food & Social Time

(Children and family members leave.)

- 1 hour:  Group members share group and individual feedback (closure)

---

# Commitment to My Family: The Father I Choose To Be (revisited)

Review your "Vision Statement: The Father I Choose To Be" *(Week 1, page 7)*. Re-write it below to reflect your revised "Commitment To My Family." Be as honest and open as you can be.

_____
_____
_____
_____
_____
_____
_____
_____
_____
_____
_____
_____
_____
_____
_____
_____
_____
_____
_____
_____
_____
_____

IMPORTANT NOTE: Bring this to graduation and be prepared to read it to your family as part of the graduation ceremony. . . and remember to invite your family (child/ren, spouse, partner, others) to attend.

# "Slam Book": Autographs and Messages

At any graduation you need a space for fellow graduates' signatures, phone numbers, and any messages . . .